Theory Paper   Grade 6   2021   A

Duration 3 hours

TOTAL MARKS
100

Candidates should answer all FIVE questions.
Write your answers on this paper – no others will be accepted.
Answers must be written clearly and neatly – otherwise marks may be lost.

1   Answer **ONE** section only, (a) or (b).

15

EITHER

(a)   Indicate **ONE** chord at each of the places marked * to accompany the following melody. You may do so by
writing roman numerals or any other recognised method of notation between the staves, **OR** by writing notes
on the staves which provide a proper harmonic structure; but use only **ONE** of these methods.

OR

(b) Complete the bass line and add a suitable figured bass as necessary, **from the first beat of bar 3**, at the places marked ∗ in this passage. If you wish to use a $\frac{5}{3}$ chord, leave the space under the asterisk blank, but $\frac{5}{3}$ chords **must** be shown when used as part of a $\frac{6}{4}\frac{5}{3}$ progression or when chromatic alteration is required.

J. B. Loeillet, Flute Sonata, Op. 5 No. 3 (adapted)

2 Writing for four-part voices (SATB) or keyboard, realise this figured bass.
Assume that all chords are $\frac{5}{3}$ unless otherwise shown.

15

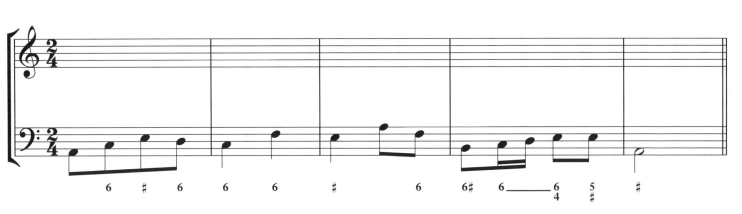

3 EITHER

(a) Continue this opening to form a complete melody for unaccompanied cello. It should end with a modulation to the dominant and should be between eight and ten bars long. Add performance directions as appropriate and write the complete melody on the staves below.

Moderato   Haydn (adapted)

OR

(b) Continue this opening for unaccompanied oboe to make a complete melody of not less than eight bars in length. You may make any modulation(s) that you wish, or none if you prefer. Add performance directions as appropriate and write the complete melody on the staves below.

Allegretto grazioso

4 Look at the extract printed opposite, which is from a piano piece, and then answer the questions below.

(a) Identify the shaded chords marked * in bars 5 and 11 by writing on the dotted lines below. Use either words or symbols. For each chord, indicate the position and show whether it is major, minor, augmented or diminished.

Bar 5 .... (3)

} Key   A major

Bar 11 .... (3)

(b) Give the full names of the notes of melodic decoration (e.g. accented passing note) marked **X**, **Y** and **Z** in the right-hand part of bars 3, 4 and 11.

X (bar 3) .... (2)

Y (bar 4) .... (2)

Z (bar 11) .... (2)

(c) Complete these statements:

(i)   There is an imperfect cadence in the tonic key in bar .... (2)

(ii)   There is a melodic interval of an augmented 5th in the right-hand part in bar .... (2)

(iii)   There is a descending chromatic semitone
(augmented unison) in the left-hand part in bar .... (2)

(d) Answer TRUE or FALSE to these statements:

(i)   The written-out ornament in the right-hand part of bar 1 could be shown as ∾. .... (2)

(ii)   There is an example of syncopation in bars 1–12 of this extract. .... (2)

(iii)   In bars 1–8, the smallest harmonic interval between
the right-hand and left-hand parts is an augmented 2nd. .... (2)

(e) From the list below, underline the name of the most likely composer of this piece.

Mozart   Chopin   Stravinsky (1)

5 Look at the extract printed opposite, which is from the third movement of Tchaikovsky's *Manfred* symphony, Op. 58, and then answer the questions below.

(a) Give the meaning of V (e.g. bar 1, second violins). .... (2)

(b) (i) Write out the parts for horns in bar 1 as they would sound at concert pitch.

(3)

(ii) Write out the parts for clarinets in bar 10 as they would sound at concert pitch.

(2)

(c) Complete these statements:

(i) On the first note of bar 9,
the highest-sounding note is played by the first oboe and the .... (2)

(ii) The first and second violin parts cross in bar(s) .... (2)

(iii) The English name for the gran cassa, an
instrument that plays in this work but **not** in this extract, is .... (2)

(iv) The cellos and double basses **sound** a note in unison in bar .... (2)

(d) Answer TRUE or FALSE to these statements:

(i) The first and second violins have to use an open string in this extract. .... (2)

(ii) The oboe is a single-reed instrument. .... (2)

(e) Describe fully the numbered and bracketed harmonic intervals **sounding** between:

1 double basses and first violins, bar 2 .... (2)

2 second violins and fourth horn, bar 5 .... (2)

3 first clarinet and second oboe, bar 11 .... (2)

BLANK PAGE

Theory Paper   Grade 6   2021   B

Duration 3 hours

TOTAL MARKS
100

Candidates should answer all FIVE questions.
Write your answers on this paper – no others will be accepted.
Answers must be written clearly and neatly – otherwise marks may be lost.

1 Answer **ONE** section only, (a) or (b).

15

EITHER

(a) Indicate **ONE** chord at each of the places marked ∗ to accompany the following melody. You may do so by writing roman numerals or any other recognised method of notation between the staves, **OR** by writing notes on the staves which provide a proper harmonic structure; but use only **ONE** of these methods.

Rameau, 'Sommeil: Rondeau tendre' from *Dardanus* (adapted)

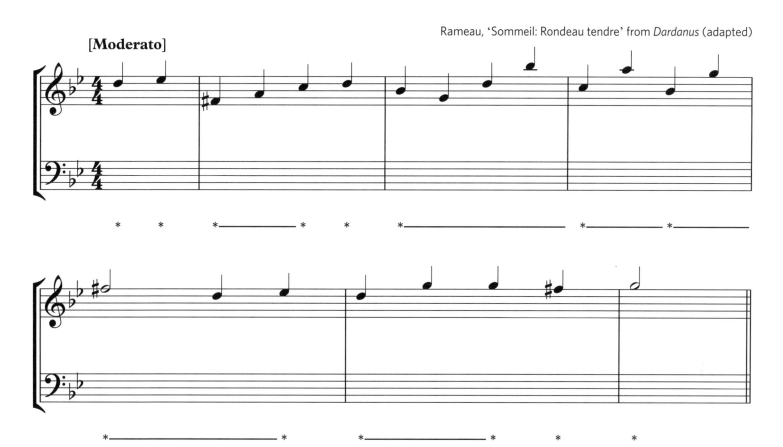

OR

(b) Complete the bass line and add a suitable figured bass as necessary, **from the last beat of bar 2**, at the places marked ∗ in this passage. If you wish to use a $\frac{5}{3}$ chord, leave the space under the asterisk blank, but $\frac{5}{3}$ chords **must** be shown when used as part of a $\frac{6}{4}\frac{5}{3}$ progression or when chromatic alteration is required.

Purcell, Chorus from *Dido and Aeneas* (adapted)

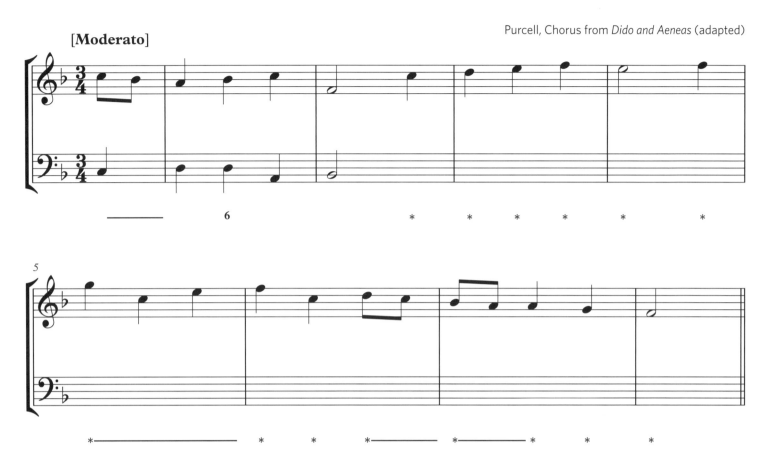

2   Writing for four-part voices (SATB) or keyboard, realise this figured bass. Assume that all chords are $\frac{5}{3}$ unless otherwise shown.

15

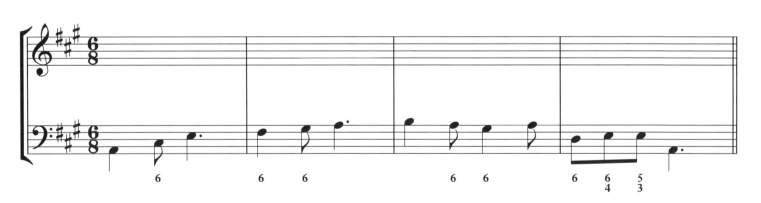

3 EITHER

(a) Continue this opening to form a complete melody for unaccompanied clarinet (at concert pitch). It should end with a modulation to the relative minor and should be between eight and ten bars long. Add performance directions as appropriate and write the complete melody on the staves below.

OR

(b) Continue this opening for unaccompanied cello to make a complete melody of not less than eight bars in length. You may make any modulation(s) that you wish, or none if you prefer. Add performance directions as appropriate and write the complete melody on the staves below.

In sanfter Bewegung

Die Ro - sen - knos - pe he - bet em - por ihr Köpf - chen bang, denn

wun - der - sam durch - be - bet hat sie der sü - ße Sang; und mehr und mehr ent -

etwas drängend

- hül - let sich ih - rer Blät - ter Füll, und ei - ne Trä - ne quil - let her -

riten.

- vor so heim - lich still.

rit.   a tempo   rit.

4 Look at the extract printed opposite, which is from a song by Wolf, and then answer the questions below.

(a) Give the meaning of:

etwas (bar 9) .... (2)

drängend (the same as **affrettando**) (bar 9) .... (2)

(b) Complete these statements:

(i) There is an arpeggiated dominant 7th chord
in root position (V^7a) in the tonic key in bar .... (2)

(ii) There is a melodic interval of a
diminished 8ve in the lower left-hand piano part in bars .... (2)

(iii) There is a note of anticipation in the soprano part in bar .... (2)

(iv) There is syncopation in the right-hand piano part in bar .... (2)

(c) Identify the shaded chords marked * in bars 3 and 4 by writing on the dotted lines below. Use either words or symbols. For each chord, indicate the position and show whether it is major, minor, augmented or diminished.

Bar 3 .... ⎫ (3)
⎬ Key   B minor
Bar 4 .... ⎭ (3)

(d) Complete this statement:

In bar 9 the music passes through the key of B minor. In bar 10 it is in the key of ....,

at the beginning of bar 12 it reaches the key of .... and at the beginning of bar 13

it reaches the key of .... (3)

(e) Answer TRUE or FALSE to these statements:

(i) The first bar in which the soprano part sounds at a
lower pitch than the top note of the right-hand piano part is in bar 5. .... (2)

(ii) The interval between the highest and
lowest notes in the soprano part is a perfect 8ve. .... (2)

5 Look at the extract printed opposite, which is from Stravinsky's ballet *Le baiser de la fée*, and then answer the questions below.

(a) Give the meaning of:

dolce (bar 1, horns) .... (2)

leggiero (bar 3, first violins) .... (2)

⊓ (e.g. bar 9, violas) .... (2)

(b) (i) Write out the parts for horns in bar 1 as they would sound at concert pitch.

(3)

(ii) Write out the part for **second** clarinet in bar 8 as it would sound at concert pitch.

(2)

(c) Complete these statements:

(i) In bar 1, the highest-**sounding** note is played by the .... (2)

(ii) A standard orchestral **non-transposing**
woodwind instrument **not** playing in this extract is the .... (2)

(iii) The first and third horns play a harmonic interval of a minor 3rd in bar .... (2)

(iv) The only string section that plays two descending
chromatic semitones (augmented unisons) in this extract is the .... (2)

(d) Describe fully the numbered and bracketed harmonic intervals **sounding** between:

1 fourth and first horns, bar 2 .... (2)

2 first violins and first clarinet, bar 7 .... (2)

3 second violins and first flute, bar 10 .... (2)

16

BLANK PAGE

Theory Paper   Grade 6   2021   C

TOTAL MARKS
100

Duration 3 hours

Candidates should answer all FIVE questions.
Write your answers on this paper – no others will be accepted.
Answers must be written clearly and neatly – otherwise marks may be lost.

1 Answer **ONE** section only, (a) or (b).

15

EITHER

(a) Indicate **ONE** chord at each of the places marked ✳ to accompany the following melody. You may do so by writing roman numerals or any other recognised method of notation between the staves, **OR** by writing notes on the staves which provide a proper harmonic structure; but use only **ONE** of these methods.

[Andante]

Storace, 'Across the Downs this Morning' from *No Song, No Supper* (adapted)

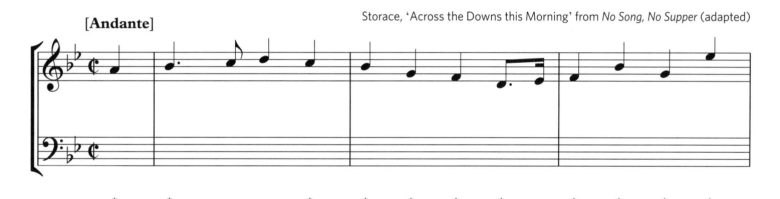

OR

(b) Complete the bass line and add a suitable figured bass as necessary, **from the last two quavers of bar 2**, at the places marked ∗ in this passage. If you wish to use a $\frac{5}{3}$ chord, leave the space under the asterisk blank, but $\frac{5}{3}$ chords **must** be shown when used as part of a $\frac{6}{4}\frac{5}{3}$ progression or when chromatic alteration is required.

Handel, Te Deum in B flat (adapted)

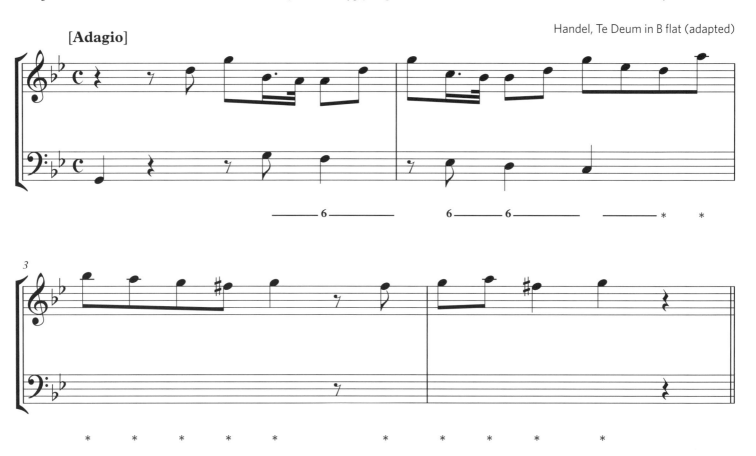

2 Writing for four-part voices (SATB) or keyboard, realise this figured bass.
   Assume that all chords are $\frac{5}{3}$ unless otherwise shown.

15

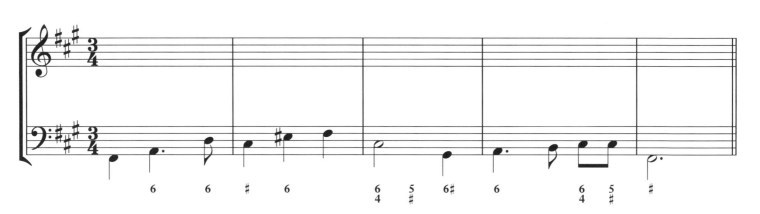

(a) Continue this opening to form a complete melody for unaccompanied bassoon. It should end with a modulation to the relative major and should be between eight and ten bars long. Add performance directions as appropriate and write the complete melody on the staves below.

OR

(b) Continue this opening for unaccompanied violin to make a complete melody of not less than eight bars in length. You may make any modulation(s) that you wish, or none if you prefer. Add performance directions as appropriate and write the complete melody on the staves below.

4 Look at the extract printed opposite, which is from a piano piece by Debussy, and then answer the questions below.

(a) Complete these statements:

(i) **un peu** (bar 13) means .... (2)

(ii) The left-hand part of bar .... forms a descending sequence (not exact) with the previous bar. (2)

(iii) There is a rising chromatic semitone
(augmented unison) in the left-hand part in bar(s) .... (2)

(iv) There is a dominant 7th chord in third inversion (V^7d) in the relative major key in bar .... (2)

(b) Write out in full the right-hand part of bar 3 as it should be played. Part of the bar is given.

(3)

(c) Name two features of the music that contribute to the change of mood at bar 17.

1 .... (1)

2 .... (1)

(d) Identify the shaded chords marked * in bars 1 and 8 by writing on the dotted lines below. Use either words or symbols. For each chord, indicate the position and show whether it is major, minor, augmented or diminished.

Bar 1 .... Key B minor (3)

Bar 8 .... Key G major (3)

(e) Compare bar 21 with bar 22 (both marked ⌐————⌐) and then name two similarities and two differences.

Similarities 1 .... (1)

2 .... (1)

Differences 1 .... (1)

2 .... (1)

(f) Answer TRUE or FALSE to this statement:

All the pitches in bar 16 sound a major 2nd higher than those in bar 6. .... (2)

23

5 Look at the extract printed opposite, which is from a viola concerto, and then answer the questions below.

(a) Give the meaning of:

più mosso (bar 4) .... (2)

arco (bar 9, first violins) .... (2)

(b) Complete these statements:

(i) On the first note of bar 3,
the solo viola **sounds** an octave higher than the .... (2)

(ii) A standard orchestral **non-transposing**
brass instrument **not** playing in this extract is the .... (2)

(c) (i) Write out the part for first clarinet in bar 9 as it would sound at concert pitch.

(2)

(ii) The notes printed below are notated at written pitch for the first and second horns shortly after the extract ends. Write out the parts (for horns in F) as they would sound at concert pitch and using the given clef. Do **not** use a key signature.

(4)

(d) Describe fully the numbered and bracketed harmonic intervals **sounding** between:

1 first oboe and first flute, bar 1 .... (2)

2 solo viola and first clarinet, bar 2 .... (2)

3 cellos and first violins, bar 9 .... (2)

(e) Answer TRUE or FALSE to these statements:

(i) The first flute and first clarinet **sound** an octave apart in bar 2. .... (2)

(ii) The cellos have to use an open string in this extract. .... (2)

(f) From the list below, underline the name of the most likely composer of this piece.

Mozart   Brahms   Bartók

(1)

24

BLANK PAGE

Theory Paper   Grade 6   2021   S

TOTAL MARKS
100

Duration 3 hours

Candidates should answer all **FIVE** questions.
Write your answers on this paper – no others will be accepted.
Answers must be written clearly and neatly – otherwise marks may be lost.

1 Answer **ONE** section only, (a) or (b).

15

EITHER

(a) Indicate **ONE** chord at each of the places marked ✳ to accompany the following melody. You may do so by writing roman numerals or any other recognised method of notation between the staves, **OR** by writing notes on the staves which provide a proper harmonic structure; but use only **ONE** of these methods.

[**Lento**]   Gibbons, Song 46

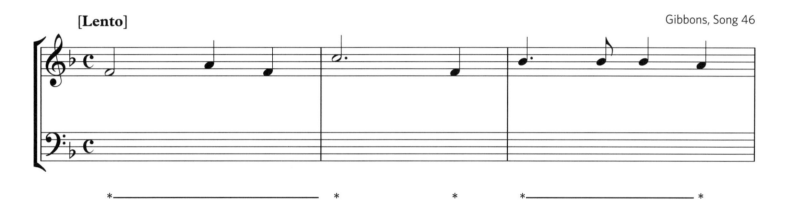

OR

(b) Complete the bass line and add a suitable figured bass as necessary, **from the last beat of bar 4**, at the places marked ✳ in this passage. If you wish to use a $\frac{5}{3}$ chord, leave the space under the asterisk blank, but $\frac{5}{3}$ chords **must** be shown when used as part of a $\frac{6}{4}\frac{5}{3}$ progression or when chromatic alteration is required.

Vivaldi, Violin Sonata, RV 756 (adapted)

2 Writing for four-part voices (SATB) or keyboard, realise this figured bass.
   Assume that all chords are $\frac{5}{3}$ unless otherwise shown.

15

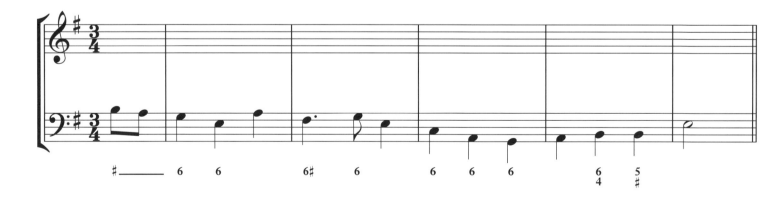

28

3 EITHER

(a) Continue this opening to form a complete melody for unaccompanied flute. It should end with a modulation to the subdominant and should be between eight and ten bars long. Add performance directions as appropriate and write the complete melody on the staves below.

Andante — Haydn (adapted)

OR

(b) Continue this opening for unaccompanied cello to make a complete melody of not less than eight bars in length. You may make any modulation(s) that you wish, or none if you prefer. Add performance directions as appropriate and write the complete melody on the staves below.

Allegretto

4 Look at the extract printed opposite, which is from a violin sonata, and then answer the questions below.

(a) Identify the shaded chords marked * in bars 10 and 14 by writing on the dotted lines below. Use either words or symbols. For each chord, indicate the position and show whether it is major, minor, augmented or diminished.

Bar 10 .... ⎫ (3)

Bar 14 .... ⎬ Key   G major (3)
⎭

(b) Complete these statements:

   (i)   There is a double stop that forms the
       harmonic interval of an augmented 4th in the violin part in bar .... (2)

   (ii) There is syncopation in the left-hand piano part in bar .... (2)

   (iii) The music passes through the dominant key in bars .... (2)

   (iv) The rhythm of the right-hand piano part
       in bars 1–2 (marked ⌐—————¬) is played by the violin .... times. (2)

(c) Answer TRUE or FALSE to these statements:

   (i)   The violin does **not** sound any notes
       in unison with the left-hand piano part in this extract.   .... (2)

   (ii) The right-hand piano part **always** sounds at a
       higher pitch than the violin part in this extract.   .... (2)

   (iii) The music is made up entirely of regular four-bar phrases.   .... (2)

(d) Compare the piano part of bars 27–28 with that of bars 29–30 (both marked ⌐—————¬) and then name one similarity and three differences.

Similarity .... (1)

Differences   1 .... (1)

            2 .... (1)

            3 .... (1)

(e) From the list below, underline one period during which this piece was written.

      1650–1750   1750–1850   1850–1950 (1)

5 Look at the extract printed opposite, which is from Lennox Berkeley's *Sinfonia concertante*, Op. 84, and then answer the questions below.

(a) Give the meaning of:

div. (e.g. bar 1, first violins) .... (2)

subito (e.g. bar 1, second violins) .... (2)

♯ (e.g. bar 3, violins) .... (2)

(b) (i) Write out the parts for horns in bar 4 as they would sound at concert pitch.

Horns 1 2 (2)

(ii) Write out the part for **first** clarinet in bar 8 as it would sound at concert pitch.

Clarinet 1 (3)

(c) Complete these statements:

(i) A standard orchestral **transposing** brass instrument **not** playing in this extract is the .... (2)

(ii) In bar 1, the lowest-sounding note is played by the .... (2)

(d) Describe fully the numbered and bracketed harmonic intervals **sounding** between:

1 second horn and second bassoon, bar 5 .... (2)

2 solo oboe and first clarinet, bar 9 .... (2)

3 cellos and violas, bar 11 .... (2)

(e) Write out the part for **first** bassoon in bars 6–7 so that it sounds at the same pitch but using the given clef.

Bassoon 1 (2)

(f) Answer TRUE or FALSE to this statement:

The largest melodic interval in the solo oboe part is a minor 7th. .... (2)